101 FURTHER USES
FOR A JOHN MAJOR

101 Uses For A John Major

101 FURTHER USES FOR A JOHN MAJOR

PATRICK WRIGHT

ANDRE DEUTSCH

First published in Great Britain in October 1994 by
André Deutsch Limited
106 Great Russell Street
London WC1B 3LJ

Second impression February 1995

Illustrations copyright © 1994 by Patrick Wright

ISBN 0 233 98897 1

Cataloguing-in-Publication data available for this title
from the British Library

Printed in Great Britain by
WBC, Bridgend

This little book is dedicated
to the entire population of
Great Britain. Oh yes.

Acknowledgments

Many thanks to the following, without whose contributions this little book would not have been such fun to produce:

May Abbott, Liz Antliff, A.J. Burgess Allen, N. Browning, David Broach, John Blagović, Karen Beal, Philip Berkin, Andrew Byron, Stephen Christie, Eva Cowan, Brian Clemens, Phil Chesterton, Bob Connell, Ernie Crosswell, John Carey, Pat Chilton, Adrian Devereux, Ruth Drysdale, Richard Davies, L. Desrosiers, Dick and friends, Aubrey Emerson, Liz Elliot, Alison Fergusson, Pete French, Shirley-Anne Fretz-Winter, S. Forster, William Fox, Mark Frayne-Johnson, Alastair Gale, Owen Griffith, Jean Louis Hory, James Hally, J.B. Hebden, Bob Heys, Nick Holder, Tim Hopkins, John & Jane Horn, Lynn & Janet Isaac, Peter Johnston, Dedwydd Jones, Nick Jackman, Jenny & Mike, Brian James, Mike Johnson, Dan Kenny, Laurie Lea, Rob Lievesley, Luke, Charles Light, Mole Mumford, James Mackay, Revd Andrew McIntosh, Chris Murfet, Donald MacMillan, Jim Maguire, R. M., Martin McCreton, Colin Noad,

Oliver Penny, Mike Pearson, Virginia Price, Peter Podmore, Robert Perry, S.C. Pollard, Matthew Parling, James Peak, Chris Pickering, C.A. Parry, Sarah Richardson, Karen Reeves, R. Rees, Wallace Reyburn, Martyn Russell, Andrew Smith, P.J. Szikora, Neville Suttle, J. Sinclair, Kate Stephen, Graham Shaw, Julia Sims, John Storry, Claire Slodzik, Jo Taylor, Stephen Thompson, Michael Turner, Lucy Taylor, Richard Taylor, Richard Tate, Anna Wakefield, Chris Waters, Katy Wix, Tish Wood, Nicolas Wood, Duncan and Joan Woolard, Simon Ward, Carla Yates, Michael Young.

Apologies to all those whose submissions arrived just too late for inclusion in this book.

Foreword

Graham was behind the bar of The Red Lion, Fernhurst, demonstrating to a small, but fascinated audience how to make tea bags from aertex underpants when Peter and I walked in.

'Landlord. Two pints of your admirably warm beer, should it please you, please,' said Peter, ostentatiously tossing a large green folder onto the bar.

'Beyond doubt,' he went on, 'you will recall referring to Prime Minister Major as "useless"* when last I entered this hostelry with whomsoever I happened to be. Well, I am here now, again, to offer you proof positive that the vast majority are of the judgement that John Major is extremely useful, and not inconsiderably so.'

'Oh yes,' I murmured.

* See *101 Uses for a John Major* by Patrick Wright and Peter Richardson

'You see, Graham, this green folder contains many hundreds of letters who believe our Premier is far more than "useless". Indeed, many have written to point out that, within just two years of assuming the highest office in the land, John Major has already attained the status of an historical footnote,' said Peter, a disdainfully superior little smile crossing his face.

'I agree,' said Graham. 'John Major is far, far more than useless.' And with that he returned to his demonstration at the other end of the bar.

Outside on the village green, several hundred Conservative ex-county councillors and defeated Euro MPs were drifting aimlessly about in the rain.

'Isn't that a marvellous sight?' said Peter. 'So many people liberated from the onerous tasks of representing their party in the city halls and in Brussels: free to spend considerably more time with their families. In no small measure, it almost makes one weep.'

'Oh yes,' I croaked.

'It is my judgement that an idea has occurred to me,' said Peter. 'Yes. Using the letters of tribute to our leader contained within this green folder, we'll compile another book in praise of Mr Major. And we'll call it *A Further 101 Uses For A John Major*. It will forever be a testament to Mr Major's . . . er, not inconsiderable usefulness. Oh yes.'

'Oh yes,' I said, weakly.

And so it was, on that rainy afternoon, the following modest tribute was devised.

JUST THE THING
TO MAKE YOUR PARTY GO WITH A SWING!

AN ARTIST'S EASEL.

PATRICK WRIGHT 94
(THANKS: VIRGINIA PRICE.)

THANKS: PHIL CHESTERTON.

A MAY POLE.

A FIGUREHEAD.

PATRICK WRIGHT 94
(THANKS JIM MAGUIRE)
WILLIAM FOX

PATRICK WRIGHT '83
(WITH THANKS TO P. FRENCH.)

OUR OLYMPIC BID.
(OR RATHER THE KIBOSH ON IT)

STARTING BLOCKS.

PATRICK WRIGHT '93
(THANKS BRIAN CLEMENS.)

PATRICK WRIGHT '94
(THANKS: JOHN & JANE HORN.)

NETBALL NET STAND.

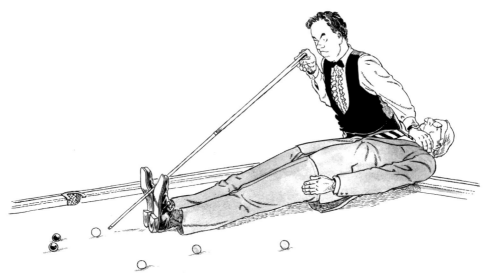

A CUE REST.

PATRICK WRIGHT.
(THANKS: NEVILLE SUTTLE)

PATRICK WRIGHT '94
(THANKS: PETER PODMORE.)

A BOWLING MACHINE – if a somewhat erratic one.

(THANKS: PETE FRENCH.)

A GOLFING TEE.

PATRICK WRIGHT '14

(THANKS: JOHN BLAGOVIC
GRAHAM SHAW
MICHAEL YOUNG)
JOAN WOOLARD.

A SURF BOARD.

PATRICK WRIGHT '94
(THANKS : MATTHEW PARLING.)

A VAULTING-HORSE.

STEP AEROBICS BENCH.

PATRICK WRIGHT.
(THANKS: JO TAYLOR.)

A POGO STICK

(THANKS: ROB LIEVESLEY.
CHARLES Light)

A CARRIAGE FOR SLIDING UPON SNOW.

PATRICK WRIGHT

PATRICK WRIGHT '93
(THANKS CHRIS MURFET.)

STABILISERS FOR A CHILD'S BIKE.

A MOTORWAY CONE.

PATRICK WRIGHT 74
THANKS - R. REES, STEPHEN THOMPSON, BOB CONNELL, RICHARD TATE, J. SINCLAIR,
T. FOOT, STEPHEN CHRISTIE, NEVILLE SUTTLE, JO TAYLOR, CHRIS MURFET,

'CATS' EYES.

THANKS JOHN BLAGOVIC

BMW XI

PATRICK WRIGHT '94
(THANKS EVA COWAN)

WINDSCREEN WIPERS.

DEVICE FOR INFLATING TYRES.

PATRICK WRIGHT '94
(THANKS: MAY ABBOTT
JIM MAGUIRE.)

PATRICK WRIGHT '94
(THANKS! L. DESROSIERS.
CARLA YATES.)

JUMP LEADS .

INEXPENSIVE AND RE-USABLE CRASH DUMMY.

PATRICK WRIGHT 94
(THANKS: CLAIRE SLODZIK.
JO TAYLOR,
STEPHEN CHRISTIE.)

PETROL PUMP ATTENDANT AT A SELF SERVICE STATION .

PATRICK WRIGHT '94
(THANKS: A.J. BURGESS-ALLEN)

A ROOF RACK

SUBSTITUTE 'SPIRIT OF ECSTASY'. FOR USE WHEN YOU HAVE TO LEAVE YOUR ROLLS ROYCE AND DON'T WANT THE REAL MASCOT STOLEN.

PATRICK WRIGHT 84
(THANKS: PETER JOHNSTON)

A NEARLY AUDIBLE WARNING ON REVERSING TRUCKS.

A PARKING METER

PATRICK WRIGHT 93
(THANKS BRIAN CLEMENS)

IMPORTANT PART OF A FORK LIFT TRUCK.

PATRICK WRIGHT: (THANKS: MARTIN McCRETON)

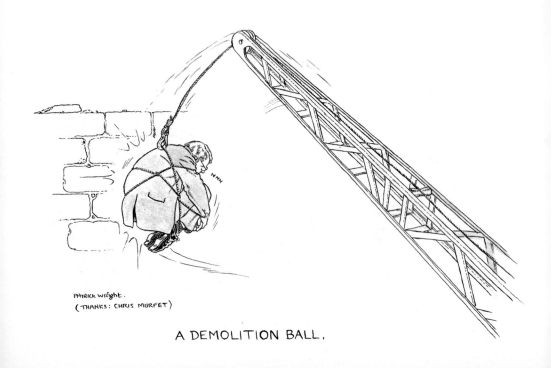

PATRICK WRIGHT.
(THANKS: CHRIS MURFET)

A DEMOLITION BALL.

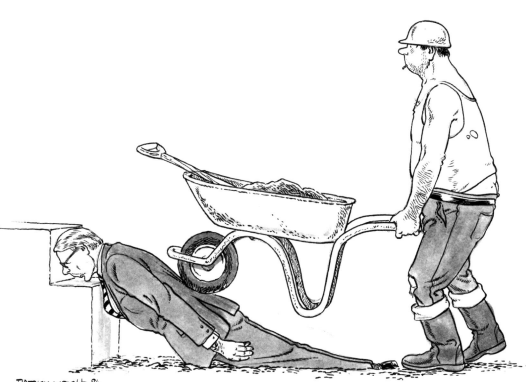

PATRICK WRIGHT 94
(THANKS ANDREW BYRON)

BUILDER'S PLANK.

A SCARE-CROW.

Patrick Wright '94

(THANKS: BRIAN CLEMENS, PETE FRENCH,
RICHARD TATE, MATTHEW PARLING,
JO TAYLOR, CHRIS MURFET, SIMON WARD
AND MASTER N. BROWNING – AGED 6)
JIM MAGUIRE.

PATRICK wright '93   (THANKS RICHARD DAVIES)

A HUNT DRAG.

FENDER ON A LONGBOAT.

THANKS: RUTH DRYSDALE
JULIA SIMS
WILLIAM FOX.

A FISHING ROD REST.

PATRICK WRIGHT '93
(THANKS P. FRENCH)

A PUNTING POLE.

PATRICK WRIGHT '94
(THANKS CHRIS MURFET.)
NICK JACKMAN.

A TENT PEG.   THANKS : J.B. HEBDEN .

AN IMPORTANT PART OF AN ANCIENT MONUMENT

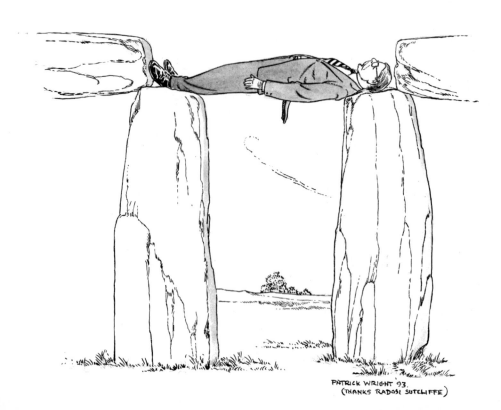

PATRICK WRIGHT '93.
(THANKS RADOSI SUTCLIFFE)

PURELY DECORATIVE FLYING BUTTRESS.

PATRICK WRIGHT '94
(THANKS: J. SINCLAIR)

PATRICK WRIGHT '94
(THANKS - JOHN BLAGOVIĆ
DONALD MACMILLAN)

A PERISCOPE .

CLEANING ROD FOR SUPER GUNS.

PATRICK WRIGHT
(THANKS: BRIAN JAMES.)

NOTE: APOLOGIES TO H.M. ARMED SERVICES — I REALISE THE MODERN
SOLDIER NO LONGER WEARS THE ABOVE UNIFORM, BUT I PREFERRED IT
WHEN THEY DID.

A CANDLE SNUFFER.

PATRICK WRIGHT '93
(WITH THANKS TO THE REVD
ANDREW McINTOSH.)

A LECTERN.

PATRICK WRIGHT '93
(THANKS KAREN REEVES)
ERNIE CROSSWELL

A CYMBAL STAND.

PATRICK WRIGHT '94
(THANKS: RICHARD TAYLOR)

A TRUMPET MUTE .

PATRICK WRIGHT `94
(THANKS : CHRIS WATERS.)

A MAJORETTE'S BATON

PATRICK WRIGHT '94
(THANKS: BOB HEYS)

ROCK SINGER'S MICROPHONE STAND.
(THANKS STEPHEN THOMPSON)

NIBBLE-
-CHOMP-
-GOBBLE-
-GULP-

PATRICK WRIGHT 94
(THANKS: CHRIS MURFET)

A LAWN MOWER.

PATRICK WRIGHT '94
(THANKS: JOAN WOOLLARD)

A SAW HORSE (THOUGH NOT A VERY STABLE ONE)

ATTRACTIVE PAPER WEIGHT.

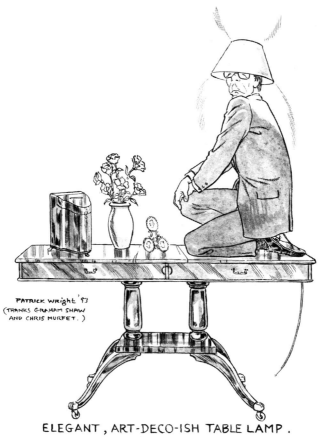

ELEGANT, ART-DECO-ISH TABLE LAMP.

PATRICK WRIGHT '93
(THANKS GRAHAM SHAW
AND CHRIS MURFET.)

ONE CORNER OF A FOUR POSTER BED.

THANKS: COLIN NOAD.

A WALL HANGING.   PATRICK WRIGHT '94
(THANKS: KATY WIX)

REMOTE CONTROLLER FOR YOUR T.V.

ER... A FART CUSHION OH, YES.

HAT AND COAT STAND.

PATRICK WRIGHT '94
(THANKS: SIMON WARD,
CHRIS MURFET,
WILLIAM FOX,
S. FORSTER.)
MICHAEL TURNER.

PATRICK WRIGHT '94
(THANKS: ANNA WAKEFIELD)
PAT CHILTON

A COAT HANGER.

A STAPLER , (ACCORDING TO LIZ ELLIOT & NICOLAS WOOD)

USEFUL DEVICE FOR CLEARING
BLOCKED SINKS.

PATRICK WRIGHT 94
(THANKS MOLE MUMFORD)

NOT VERY PRACTICAL EGG TIMER.

THANKS : PETE FRENCH.

BOTTLE OPENER.

PATRICK WRIGHT '94
(THANKS : CHRIS MURFET,
S, FORSTER.)

A DEVICE FOR ILLUMINATING YOUR FRIDGE.
(VERY USEFUL, OH YES.)

PATRICK WRIGHT '94
(THANKS: TIM HOPKINS)

PATRICK WRIGHT '93
(WITH THANKS TO P. FRENCH)

A SALAD SHAKER.

A COSY DOG BASKET.

PATRICK WRIGHT '94
(THANKS SARAH RICHARDSON)

A FISH TANK AERATOR .

A PARROT PERCH

PATRICK WRIGHT 93
(THANKS BRIAN CLEMENS)

IMPRESSIVE HEARTH RUG

A BANANA SKIN GRADER.

PATRICK WRIGHT 94
(THANKS DAVID BROACH
AND SIMON WARD.)
AND JOAN WOOLARD.

A WASHING LINE .

A SHOWER CURTAIN, ALTHOUGH IN NO SMALL MEASURE
A NOT VERY EFFECTIVE ONE. OHNO.

PATRICK WRIGHT '94
(THANKS! LUCY TAYLOR)

STAND AT A COCONUT SHY.

PATRICK WRIGHT 94
(THANKS: KAREN REEVES.)
MIKE JOHNSON.
PETE FRENCH.

USEFUL DEVICE FOR LIGHTING MATCHES.

THANKS: ALASDAIR GALE

PATRICK WRIGHT 94
(THANKS: J. SINCLAIR.
STEPHEN THOMPSON.)

HANDY C.D. STORAGE UNIT .

USEFUL DEVICE FOR MEASURING THE DEPTH OF WATER.

PATRICK WRIGHT '93
(THANKS PETE FRENCH
AND CHRIS MURFET)

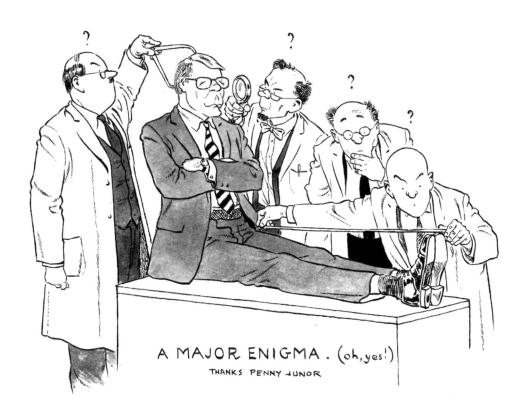

A MAJOR ENIGMA. (oh, yes!)

THANKS PENNY JUNOR

A SPEAKING CLOCK.

PATRICK WRIGHT. '93
(THANKS, AGAIN, P. FRENCH)

DEVICE FOR DETECTING EARTH TREMORS.

FERTILISER.

PATRICK WRIGHT '94
(THANKS ADRIAN DEVEREUX.)

USED CAN COLLECTION POINT.

PATRICK WRIGHT 94
(THANKS : ANDREW SMITH)

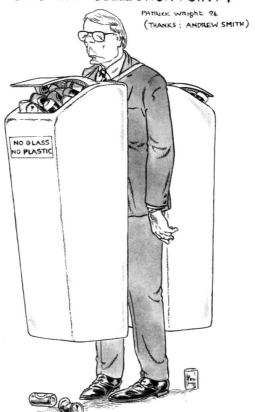

NO GLASS
NO PLASTIC

A POOPA-SCOOPA.

PATRICK WRIGHT '94
(THANKS; NEVILLE SUTTLE,
R.M. OF EDINBURGH)

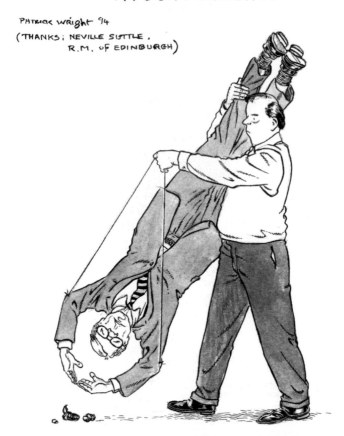

PATRICK WRIGHT '94
(THANKS – JIM MAGUIRE)

PUB GRUB MENU HOLDER.

AN AGENT FOR TERRY MAJOR.

PATRICK WRIGHT '93

PATRICK WRIGHT '93
(WITH THANKS TO LIZ ANTLIFF.)

HAPPY CHRISTMAS

A YULE LOG.

PATRICK WRIGHT '93
(THANKS CHRIS MURFET.)